THE MANGA BIBLE

NT - RAW

About the authors

SIKU (concept and art)

Siku is one of Britain's leading comic book/concept artists, having worked for *2000AD*; producing titles such as 'Judge Dredd', 'Slaine' and a strip he co-created called 'Pan-African Judges'. He has also worked for Marvel UK and COM X and has been credited on a number of computer games such as *Evil Genius*. More recently, he has been developing concept work for TV commercials and producing freelance work for Nickelodeon IP and promos.

Siku's works are published in several books and has appeared on TV interviews, channel 4's *The Big Breakfast* and channel 5's *Chris Moyle's Show*.

He is currently a final year undergraduate at the London School of Theology.

AKINSIKU (script)

Akin Akinsiku was born in 1968 in London. He spent the next 15 years in a lovely country called Nigeria where became obsessed with Japanese animation and kung-fu movies. He originally wanted to become a Superhero. That was before he started experimenting by drawing ugly pictures, writing ugly stories and watching TV 10 hours a day. He perfected this 'art' while studying fine arts in Nigeria, and Animation in England.

Today, he gets paid to draw ugly pictures, write ugly stories and make TV 10 hours a day for Nickelodeon. Someday he would love to clone medical students or Ninjas. He still wants to become a Superhero.

Acknowledgements

SIKU

The girl in the last chapter of this book is based on my younger daughter whose courage and peace in the face of ill health is nothing less than exemplary Christian testimony. A testimony which I find perplexing and humbling. Respect to my wife who lost her husband while I stayed awake burning the midnight oil. A shout out to my beautiful older daughter and brilliant stepson who assisted me in this work.

A mention of my tutor Dr Conrad Gempf who checked my work. He sort of sneaks up on you (theologically speaking). Along with the encyclopaedic Dr Paul Blackham – they are both comic book aficionados who have been of some influence in my growing appreciation of the scriptures. Word up to Rico Tice who mentored me for a while, and to Ed. My whole family; a mother who knows how to pray and my brother who put words to my concepts, a man after my heart.

Finally, what does one say to the master of the universe my Lord Jesus Christ? Words are never enough. Thank you for calling me when I knew no better.

'nuff said.

AKINSIKU

To three generations of Akinsiku; mum Ibiye, Lulu and Themba Sileola. To mum – you are a living embodiment of 'man shall not live by bread alone'. Still standing. To Lulu and Themba 'kaiga' Sile. Thanks for rescuing the man on the moon – I can't wait for you both to walk under the Naija sun. And last but not the least , to the 'Ancient of Days'. I have loved you, I have wrestled with you. Now I get to put my words into your mouth. I am not worthy. World without end.

Thanks also to Ed Chatelier, Edge Group for setting it up.

THE MANGA BIBLE

NT - RAW

concept and art:
siku

script:
akinsiku

The Manga Bible – New Testament
Copyright © 2007 by Siku

First published in Great Britain in 2007

The right of Siku to be identified as the Author of the Work
has been asserted by him in accordance with the Copyright,
Designs and Patents Act 1988.

With thanks to: Akindele Akinsiku (script) and Ed Chatelier
of the Edge Group

1

British Library Cataloguing in Publication Data
A record for this book is available from the British Library

ISBN 978 0340 910436

Printed and bound in Italy by
Legoprint S.P.A

The paper and board used in this paperback are natural
recyclable products made from wood grown in sustainable forests.
The manufacturing processes conform to the environmental
regulations of the country of origin.

Hodder & Stoughton
A Division of Hodder Headline Ltd
338 Euston Road
London NW1 3BH
www.hodderchristianbooks.co.uk

www.themangabible.co.uk

Read This First!

The Manga Bible – NT is an adaptation of the New Testament of the Holy Bible. It tells the story of Jesus' life as a man, living among us, and the formation and adventures of the first ever church, in graphic novel form.

It does *not* claim to tell all the stories or cover all the teaching of the New Testament, but is intended to provide a helpful 'first step' into the Bible; to give you, the reader, a taste of the most important themes and characters, and a basic idea of what it's all about!

The creators and publishers hope that **The Manga Bible** will inspire you to read more of the full-text Bible. The New Testament is an amazing book – the world's all-time best-seller – which can offer guidance, comfort and wisdom for life if you take the time to read it properly. There are plenty of study Bibles and commentaries available that help explain some of the more difficult passages.

To help you make the link between **The Manga Bible** and the original scriptures, we have provided small 'Want to know more?' captions throughout the artwork. These give you the Bible references on which the preceding few panels of comic strip are based. If you want to know more about the story you have just read, look up the reference in the New Testament and read the 'official' version there.

The Bible reference is arranged as Book:Chapter:Verse. So, for example, 'Matthew 4:1–11' means the Bible passage is in the book of Matthew, chapter 4, verses 1 to 11. Most Bibles should have a contents page to help you find the right book easily.

WANT TO KNOW MORE?
LUKE 10:25-37

HEROD'S PALACE.

'WE HAVE COME LOOKING FOR THE ONE BORN KING OF THE JEWS... TO PAY OUR RESPECTS.'

'ENRAGED, HEROD TRIED TO TRICK US INTO LEADING HIM TO THE NEWBORN MESSIAH.'

'OF COURSE, WE NEVER REPORTED BACK TO HIM. INSTEAD, WE WARNED THE CHILD'S FAMILY.'

FLEE! ESCAPE TO EGYPT! HEROD WILL TRY TO KILL THE BOY.

WE NEVER RETURNED TO HEROD. IT WAS THEN HE TURNED HIS SOLDIERS AGAINST THE CHILDREN OF BETHLEHEM, AND MURDERED THEM.

TWO YEARS LATER.

HEROD WAS DEAD. HIS KINGDOM WAS DIVIDED AMONGST HIS SONS – HEROD ANTIPAS, PHILIP THE TETRARCH AND ARCHELAUS.

ON HEARING OF THE TYRANT'S DEATH, A CERTAIN CARPENTER, HIS WIFE AND CHILD RETURNED TO ISRAEL FROM EGYPT.

HEROD'S DEEPEST FEARS WERE TO BE FULFILLED THROUGH THIS ONE THAT GOT AWAY. THE BABY WOULD BECOME KNOWN AS JESUS THE MESSIAH (OR CHRIST).

WANT TO KNOW MORE? matthew 1:18-2:23

WANT TO KNOW MORE? MATTHEW 4:1-11

A CERTAIN MAN WAS TRAVELLING FROM JERUSALEM TO JERICHO.

SUDDENLY.

KILL HIM!

TAKE HIS MONEY FIRST - LOOKS LIKE HE'S LOADED!

THE ROBBERS BEAT HIM AND LEFT HIM FOR DEAD.

BY CHANCE, A **VICAR** CAME BY.

A VICTIM OF ROBBERS! HMM... BEST LEAVE HIM. I DON'T WANT TO GET INVOLVED.

AND ALSO A **CHOIRMASTER**.

I'LL PRETEND I HAVEN'T SEEN HIM. SEEMS LIKE A GOOD PLACE TO CROSS THE ROAD, ANYWAY.

LATER, A **FOREIGNER** (A SAMARITAN) CAME ALONG THE ROAD.

BALAAM, I THINK THERE'S A WOUNDED MAN ON THE ROADSIDE. LOOKS LIKE A VICTIM OF ROBBERY.

YOU'RE BARELY ALIVE! I'M NO DOCTOR BUT I'VE JUST PASSED MY FIRST AID COURSE, SO I'LL DO MY BEST TO FIX YOU UP GOOD.

WANT TO KNOW MORE?
Luke 10:25-37

THE FOREIGNER BROUGHT THE WOUNDED MAN TO AN INN AND TOOK CARE OF HIM.

THE NEXT DAY, WHEN THE FOREIGNER DEPARTED, HE GAVE THE INN KEEPER ENOUGH MONEY TO LOOK AFTER THE INJURED MAN...

'SO WHICH OF THESE MEN ACTED AS A NEIGHBOUR TO THE WOUNDED MAN?'

WANT TO KNOW MORE?
JOHN 3:1-21

WANT TO KNOW MORE?
matthew 21:33-46

WE'VE GOT A SPECIAL MOCK TRIAL SET UP JUST FOR YOU, JESUS. FIRST – A LITTLE BIT OF TORTURE TO SOFTEN YOU UP FOR 'INTERROGATION'. AND GUESS WHO YOU'VE GOT FOR JUDGE, JURY AND EXECUTIONER?

'...YOUR BESTEST FRIEND IN THE WORLD – CAIAPHAS, THE HIGH PRIEST.'

JESUS, IS IT TRUE THAT YOU THREATENED TO DESTROY THE TEMPLE AND REBUILD IT IN THREE DAYS?

HY DON'T U DEFEND URSELF? ARE YOU RIST, THE N OF THE LESSED?

I AM. AND YOU WILL SEE ME SITTING AT THE RIGHT HAND OF GOD.

BLASPHEMY! WE DON'T NEED WITNESSES ANY MORE. SURELY THIS WARRANTS THE DEATH PENALTY?

THEN THE HIGH PRIEST TORE HIS CLOTHES IN RITUAL LAMENT.

THE MOB OF ELDERS AND SADDUCEES SPAT AT JESUS AND SLAPPED AND HIT HIM WHILE CONDEMNING HIM TO DEATH.

EARLY NEXT MORNING, JESUS WAS DELIVERED TO PONTIUS PILATE, THE ROMAN GOVERNOR OF JUDEA.

PILATE, AS YOU ARE THE ONLY ONE WHO CAN AUTHORISE AN EXECUTION, WE HAVE BROUGHT THE CASE TO YOU.

I'LL HAVE A LOOK AT THIS MAN.

ARE YOU THE KING OF THE JEWS?

ARE YOU ASKING FOR YOURSELF OR DID OTHERS TELL YOU THIS ABOUT ME?

AM I A JEW? YOUR OWN PEOPLE HAVE DELIVERED YOU TO ME.

MY KINGDOM IS NOT OF THIS WORLD. IF IT WERE, THEN MY SERVANTS WOULD FIGHT TO SAVE ME FROM THE JEWS.

ARE YOU A KING, THEN?

YOU ARE RIGHT THAT I AM A KING. FOR THIS CAUSE I WAS BORN, THAT I SHOULD BEAR WITNESS TO THE TRUTH. EVERYONE WHO IS OF THE TRUTH HEARS MY VOICE.

WANT TO KNOW MORE? Matthew 26:57-68

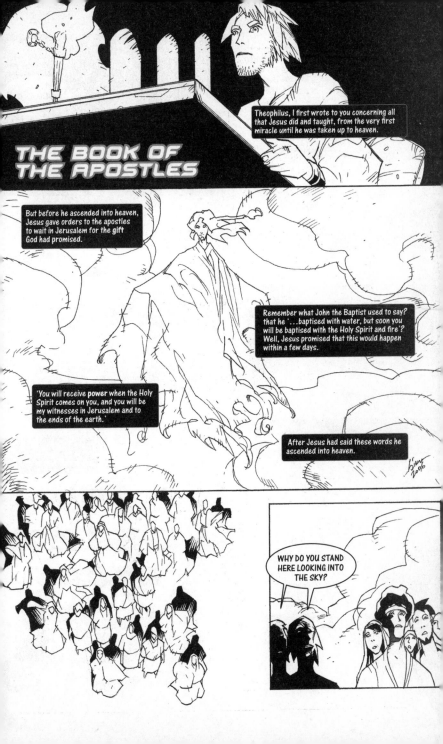

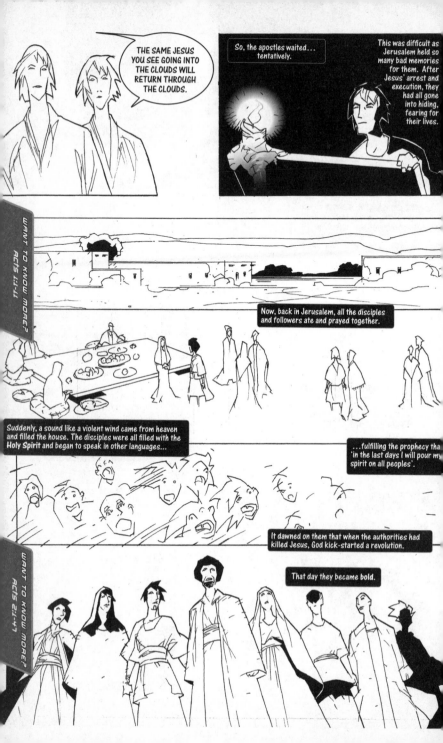

WANT TO KNOW MORE?
ACTS 1:1-11

WANT TO KNOW MORE?
ACTS 2:1-47

AND SO, SAUL THE PERSECUTOR BECAME **PAUL** THE CHRISTIAN CONVERT.

IRONIC, ISN'T IT, THAT A MAN DEDICATED TO ERADICATING A CAUSE SHOULD BECOME ONE OF ITS MOST POWERFUL APOSTLES?

IT'S KINDA HARD TO SAY NO TO GOD... ESPECIALLY IF HE ASKS YOU NICELY... IN PERSON!

AT THAT TIME, PETER BEGAN TO PREACH TO THE GENTILES (NON-JEWS). FIRST HE SPOKE TO **CORNELIUS**, A ROMAN OFFICER. THIS WAS REVOLUTIONARY.

NOW WE GENTILES CAN BELIEVE WITHOUT BECOMING JEWISH OR BEING CIRCUMCISED. WE CAN ALSO BE BAPTISED AND RECEIVE THE HOLY SPIRIT.

HOWEVER, **KING HEROD AGRIPPA** ALSO BEGAN TO PERSECUTE THE CHURCH. HE MURDERED JAMES AND, WHEN HE SAW THAT IT PLEASED THE JEWS, WENT ON TO ARREST PETER.

AN ANGEL OF THE LORD BROKE PETER FREE, BUT HEROD EXECUTED THE PRISON GUARDS IN CHARGE.

BUT AT THE HEIGHT OF HEROD'S POWER, GOD STRUCK HIM DEAD.

HEROD THOUGHT HIMSELF A GOD, BUT **WORMS** ATE HIS BODY ALIVE.

WANT TO KNOW MORE? ACTS 9:1-31

WANT TO KNOW MORE? ACTS 10:1-48

WANT TO KNOW MORE? ACTS 12:1-24

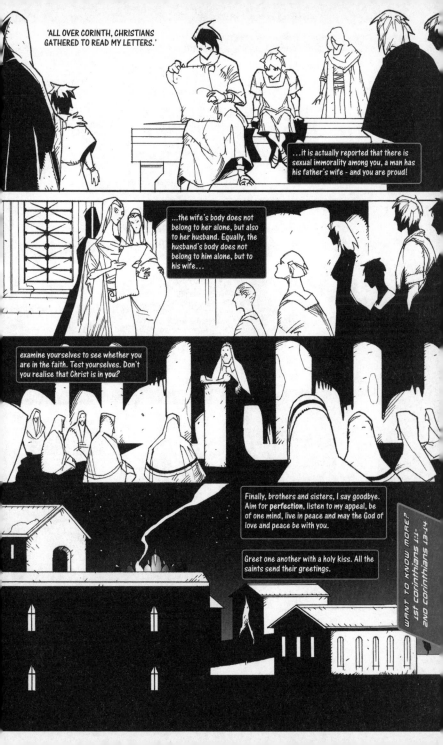

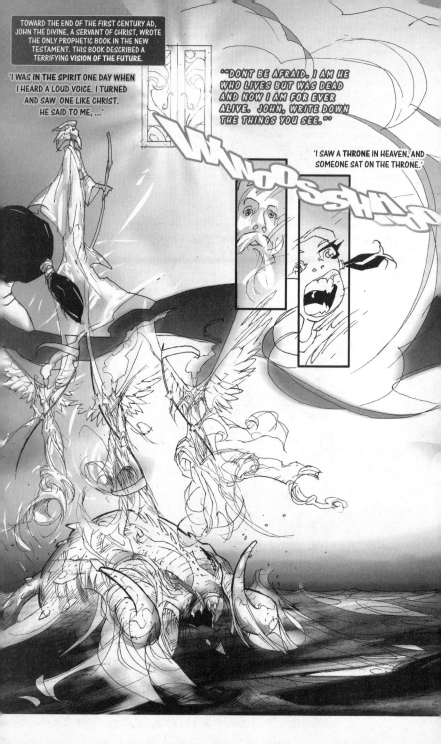

Creating The Manga Bible

Akin, left, and Siku

Taking a break from adding the finishing touches to the New Testament pages, artist Siku and his brother Akin, who wrote the script, were interviewed by broadcaster and journalist Mike Rimmer about the creative process behind *The Manga Bible*.

MIKE: Siku, if I was into comics what would I have seen of yours?

SIKU: You would have seen my stuff in *2000 AD*. My style is essentially modern-British and *2000 AD*, although recently that has changed. My forms are more elongated. More accentuated. It's still Western but not that run-of-the-mill, general, 'one size fits all' Western comic book style any more.

How Manga fits into that is that when you incorporate some of the general principles of Manga with my style you get something that's a little bit different, like a hybrid. Though you would still call it Manga.

MIKE: So *The Manga Bible* is your hybrid rather than a pure Manga form?

SIKU: It's difficult to say 'pure Manga' because all Mangas tend to be quite different. Especially now, where everyone is kind of individual. That's probably come up because Manga artists themselves are influenced by Western comic books and by Western artists and concept artists and designers. I wouldn't say there is one Manga style.

MIKE: In cartoon world there are goodies and there are baddies aren't there? There are certain stylistic ways in which you portray them. How have those things come into what you've done? Because you've been talking about humanising Jesus but good guys in cartoons tend to be slightly larger than life, don't they?

SIKU: Yes. Where I come from in comic books is really dark science-fiction. Dark and gritty, that's my background. I can't escape that. So I don't see Jesus as Bambi, basically. The Manga style I've chosen isn't the big-eyed, glassy-type Manga. It's kind of more serious; more Anime.

Jesus is not cuddly in this Manga book. In the desert, he's actually more terrifying than Satan. He's hooded and his face is shaded. The Devil is more vanilla-flavoured looking — very, very plain. I've deliberately made Jesus more imposing than anyone else throughout the story, and darker. He's creepier.

I don't just see God as a shining light thing. I also see him as a dark, brooding force. I've tried to inject that into how I see Jesus.

MIKE: Is that in Scripture or is that you imposing your own view on what's there in the Bible?

SIKU: I think there are dark aspects to God. Certain things we can't explain. Certain things seem brutal. The way, for example, he allows evil to carry on. 'Why don't you just stop it, God?' But he doesn't. And I think that's dark. I can't explain it and I don't think anyone can.

I see Jesus as making a very shrewd decision to die for humanity. And, even with everyone else not really understanding what he was doing, still having to go on and take that decision. Going into the garden and praying to God, 'If it is possible, let this thing pass. Having said that, your will be done.' I think those are dark moments.

I think over-emphasising the sweet parts of Scripture is the problem.

MIKE: I'm interested to see where you've come from. How did you become a Christian?

SIKU: I became a Christian when I was eleven, in Nigeria. I was playing football on Sunday morning in front of the chapel. They were having church service. Then one of my friends, who wasn't a believer, said, 'Don't you go to church?' And for some reason I felt guilty. Don't ask me why. So I walked in. They were praying the last prayer and the guy leading said, 'Jesus loves you.' And for some reason I understood the Gospel. I don't know how I understood the Gospel. But I understood it and I knew I needed to be saved. Don't ask me how. I don't know. And that day I got saved.

MIKE: Are you hoping that *The Manga Bible* might have a similar impact on a kid reading it?

SIKU: Who knows? The Holy Spirit does what he does, doesn't he?

MIKE: If he can get you from football into church then he could get somebody who's reading it to understand the Gospel.

SIKU: I think that my contribution will have some impact. I don't know how much impact. That's left to the Holy Spirit and I'm happy with that.

MIKE: Akin, you are responsible for writing the scripts for *The Manga Bible*...

AKIN: Basically, the two of us discuss the whole project, and different storylines, then come to a consensus about which blocks of stories to actually compile together and how they all interlink. So, we have a verbal discussion about the script and then my brother goes away and plots all the scenes, kind of like creating a storyboard. That gives him the opportunity to create visuals of dramatic scenes. Then I work out how to fit the story into the pictures. Which can be an ordeal! But it's very satisfying.

MIKE: Is there much falling out between the two of you?

AKIN: Not so far! It's a tried and tested technique. We did it years ago when we did stuff for *Judge Dredd Megazine* – *'A Pan-African Story'*. That was really, really difficult because I came up with a story and then he did the drawings and then I put the words in. This time, because we were working to a text that already exists, in some ways it was less troublesome.

SIKU: I've not seen this done anywhere, where the script is basically the storyboard. Akin has written dialogue to fit the pictures. We've been working together for years so I can really trust the way that he would interpret how I've broken down the dialogue. So I've left it to him purely. I like what he's done.

MIKE: What about the whole structure of adapting the Bible – a hefty book – and making it into what you've got here, which is much shorter? How difficult was it to cut bits out?

SIKU: Excruciating, actually! Very, very difficult. But when you have to really cramp things down to a very small size, sometimes something magical happens. In a way, it's forced us to be disciplined. We've asked ourselves: 'What do we want to get out of this?' One thing in particular was to bring out the humanity of Christ. So that when you read it, you see that he was actually a human being, just like us. I think that was very, very important to get through.

Secondly, it was important to set the scenes as though you were watching a movie. So it concentrates on stories that were dynamic rather than just having talking heads. I'd concentrate on stories or pick up parables, for example, that had some people moving around and doing things. Where you could have good shots, good composition – I think that was my criteria.

MIKE: But were you just driven by what would make a good story?

SIKU: It's funny, you know – I would say the Holy Spirit is probably driven by that too! I think Jesus was driven by that. That's why his parables were incredible. They were so brilliant that we have a different section for them. When you read it from that point of view you say, 'Hang on, this guy is actually a very good story teller!'

So yeah, we were driven by that singular motive rather than just moralising and giving people dictates: 'Do this. Don't do that.' By telling the story, people will get whatever message they need to get.

MIKE: I can imagine that it would be quite easy to do the Gospels and to do Acts. Those would be quite straightforward to adapt. But the letters I would imagine would be more of a challenge?

SIKU: The Gospels were the toughest challenge. Give a script to four expert film directors and you'll get four very different films. That's what the Gospel writers did. These guys didn't care too much about timeline – they were more concerned about what message they were trying to give, who they were talking to, how they were to present it.

So we had to tease out how events happened chronologically. Whether certain events were duplicated or whether they actually happened at different places at different times. That was very hard because you had to read the Gospels several times over. So that was tough.

AKIN: And then we got on to the letters and that just opened up a totally different can of worms. It was like learning a different language. Where was Paul when he wrote this letter? When he wrote the letters to the Romans or the Corinthians where was he writing them from? Of course, that's not in the Bible.

One of the difficulties of the Bible for a lot of people, including me, is that parts, especially the letters, seem quite contained and isolated. It's nice to give them a reference outside of the book so that you can actually place them in a real place and a real time.

So we had to go outside of the books to actually pick up the information. It's not made up out of nowhere, it's from years of actual research and study and cross-referencing, tried and tested historical records outside of the Bible. To create a background for the story.

MIKE: What about the book of Revelation? Four pages! That's it?

SIKU: Yes, four pages for the book of Revelation! If you did a whole book on Revelation then you could really explore all the different elements in it. If you're working on the book of the New Testament, when you get to the book of Revelation you're going into a different genre. So you've got to find a way to make this genre, which is almost like fantasy, fit in. That's quite hard.

So, we've created a device. A twelve-year-old girl in hospital is reading the Bible and she drifts off, sleeping. And then she gets into John's world where John is approached by Jesus, and she's actually there. She's there with John and sees everything. And in the end Jesus looks at her and winks at her and it's like, 'Oh! He saw me!' And then she's back in her bed and she wakes up. That's what we've done to kind of humanise it a little bit.

MIKE: Akin, the language that you've used is more, for want of a better expression, 'street'.

AKIN: Yes. In the very early stage I had to think, 'Okay, what exactly are we trying to do? Do we want to present the people with a language that reflects the old world? Or do we actually want to communicate something more contemporary? Something that's more relevant to the way people relate to each other and the kind of books people read, comic books?'

So I consciously decided that I was going to break down the stiff language of the King James version and make it more accessible to people. Just kind of loosen things up a little bit. Because at the end of the day, I don't expect people to go to church with *The Manga Bible* and open it up while they're preaching, you know?

To be honest with you, when I was writing it I had in mind people that have never been to church before. People that have presuppositions about Christianity and Christians. We live in a time where people are very hostile towards Christianity and it's a hostility that is born out of ignorance. A lot of people don't know a lot of things about Christianity but they assume they know. Hopefully

someone will pick this up and say, 'You know what? Actually Jesus is not what I thought he was. Paul is not what I thought he was. The Bible isn't what I thought it was. It's something totally different.' They might hopefully then move on to the original material and start reading. Hopefully a more contemporary interpretation.

Even for Christians, penetrating the archaic language can be difficult.

MIKE: So are you just trying to make Jesus cool again?

AKIN: I wouldn't say cool, because cool is very flaky. Just more accessible.

You can listen to the original, longer version of this interview at **www.themangabible.com**

Listen to Mike Rimmer on Cross Rhythms: **www.crossrhythms.co.uk**

SKETCHES

These next few pages show the development of characters, storyboards and layouts. Many of these characters were designed without knowing who they would be in the final draught; the characters themselves suggested who they would become.

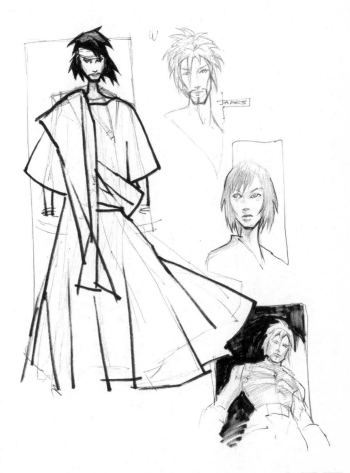

character studies

CORRUPT GU

PILATE ?

ROMAN JAILER

NIGER

SIMON THE ZEALOT

PAUL

M.B 77

JUDAS
ISCAROT

PETER

SUPER
DEFORMED

M.B 79

concept/storyboard

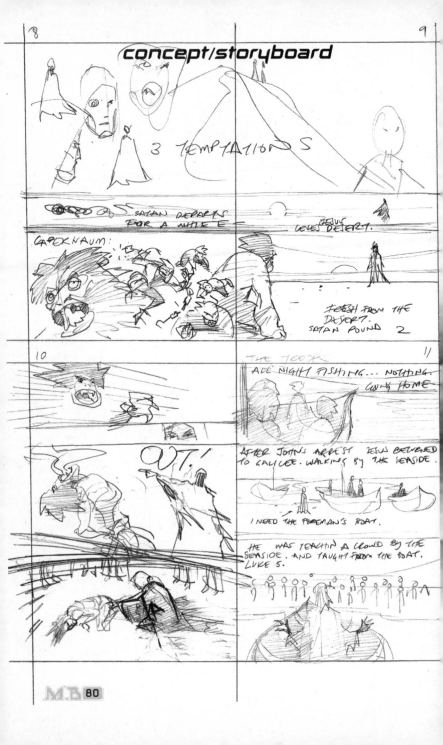

3 TEMPTATIONS

SATAN DEPARTS
FOR A WHILE

LEAVES JESUS
DESERT.

CAPERNAUM:

FRESH FROM THE
DESERT.
SATAN ROUND 2

THE TROOPS
ALL NIGHT FISHING... NOTHING.
GOING HOME

OUT!

AFTER JOHN'S ARREST JESUS RETURNED
TO GALILEE. WALKING BY THE SEASIDE.

I NEED THE FOREMAN'S BOAT.

HE WAS TEACHING A CROWD BY THE
SEASIDE. AND TAUGHT FROM THE BOAT.
LUKE 5.

M.B 83

inks

All about the Holy Bible

Explaining the Bible

The Manga Bible should not be treated as a replacement for the original Holy Bible. It is an adaptation – an *interpretation* – of a book that hundreds of millions of people believe to be the most important book ever written.

In fact, the Bible is more than just a book. When we open it, we see that it is a collection of sixty-six books. In fact, the word 'Bible' comes from the plural of a word meaning 'books'. It is a collection of religious writings written over a long period of time (as many as sixteen centuries may have separated the writing of the first book from the last) by different authors.

The complete Bible consists of two main parts: the Old Testament and the New Testament. 'Testament' means 'agreement' and the two parts describe the main agreements that God made with his people. These include the giving of the Law to Moses and the Israelites (in the Old Testament) and, of supreme importance for Christians, the life, death and resurrection of Jesus, which led to a completely new understanding of how people could relate to God (in the New Testament).

But the Bible is more than a set of contracts. One of the most amazing things about the Bible is the huge variety of material in it. Even the New Testament, which is approximately only a quarter the size of the complete Bible, contains writing styles as diverse as biography, historical adventure, parables, letters and prophecy.

This edition of *The Manga Bible* contains the New Testament. Look out for the Old Testament coming later this year!

The story of the New Testament

The New Testament begins with the story of how a craftsman from a small village in an unfashionable neighbourhood became the most important figure in history. The Jews were already waiting for a particular kind of Messiah to rescue them, and they certainly weren't expecting anyone like Jesus. No one knew much about Jesus of Nazareth except that he was likeable and respected.

Soon, stories were coming from other villages about the miracles Jesus had performed. He talked to people too, in a way that made them listen. He said that the strict religious teaching of the day had made God seem far away from people, whereas God was actually right there on earth for everyone to know. He said that people could go straight to God for forgiveness.

He didn't care what the Romans or Herod, the local ruler, or even the religious leaders thought of him. He just told people about the kingdom of God. People would say that he often seemed happy and sad at the same time. He was a mystery and people flocked to him. He fed thousands when there was no food available; he raised a friend from the dead; he walked on water, and did many more amazing things.

Jesus was eventually executed at the age of just thirty-three and, for some people, that was that. He was asking for it, some thought. His followers were shell-shocked. Then, slowly at first, word was passed through the villages of Galilee saying that he was alive. Some of his followers claimed to have seen him. They talked about God living inside them and fire coming down on their heads; and they began to teach the same radical messages that Jesus had preached.

Jesus' followers soon had a leader, Paul, who was a Roman citizen and who spread the news about Jesus far and wide by visiting and 'church planting' and by letter writing. They killed

Paul eventually, but by then he had made many new Christians, followers of Jesus Christ, all over Asia Minor. Despite the Romans' attempts to get rid of Jesus' followers, their numbers just kept growing, particularly among non-Jews. Followers became known as 'Christians' for the first time, and eventually spread to the heart of the empire, Rome herself.

creating the new testament

When the earliest Christians first began meeting together, stories of Jesus were recited by those who had known him personally. But, before long, churches identified a collection of the most important records. These included the reliable first-hand accounts of the life of Jesus, known as the Gospels (the books of Matthew, Mark, Luke and John), and stories about those who established the church after his death (the book of Acts). The documents also included letters written by some of the major church leaders, such as Paul, James and John, offering teaching and encouragement to the members of new churches that were being established in towns and cities further afield. The final book, Revelation, is a letter too, but differs from the others in that the writer, John, describes an incredible vision of Jesus, heaven and the end of history. It is a highly symbolic book and has been interpreted in many different ways, but it seems clear that its central message is God's ultimate victory over evil.

is it true?

Why do people place such faith in the words of the Bible? How can we trust such a diverse collection of documents put together 2000 years ago (almost 4000 in the case of the Old Testament)? Well, there are a number of factors that have led hundreds of thousands of people to conclude that the amazing stories of the Bible really happened:

It is historically and archaeologically accurate. There is plenty of scientific evidence that proves places described in the Bible really existed and events really did take place.

We have a wealth of manuscript evidence for many biblical books. There are many more ancient copies of the books of the Bible than of any of the great Greek or Roman classics, on which we base so much other historical 'truth' (Julius Caesar's Gallic War survives in only nine or ten copies while we have over 5000 copies of the New Testament in the original Greek alone).

Many of the biblical writers made accurate predictions about the future. Many of the Old Testament predictions and prophecies were fulfilled by Jesus.

But perhaps most importantly of all...

... it has been successfully 'tried and tested' by millions of people around the world. Those people who have taken a step of faith and decided to trust the words of the Bible have found that its teaching is relevant and appropriate as a blueprint for living in the modern world, that God is true to his written promises and that it is possible to have a real, dynamic, and personal relationship with him.